ONE LIGHT
MANY LAMPS

Written and Illustrated by
Victoria Jones

RADHA SOAMI SATSANG BEAS

Published by:
J.C. Sethi, Secretary
Radha Soami Satsang Beas
Dera Baba Jaimal Singh
Punjab 143 204, India

For internet orders, please visit:
www.rssb.org

For book orders within India, please write to:
Radha Soami Satsang Beas
BAV Distribution Centre, 5 Guru Ravi Dass Marg
Pusa Road, New Delhi 110 005

Other children's books by the same publisher:

The Journey of the Soul

First edition 2009

16 15 14 13 12 11 10 09   8 7 6 5 4 3 2 1

ISBN 978-81-8256-815-0

Printed in India by:
Thomson Press (India) Ltd.

This book is dedicated to the One
who is the many...

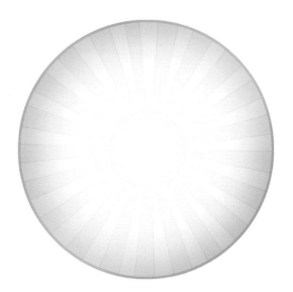

Once upon a time,
a soul was
about to be born
on earth.

Maybe that soul
was you...

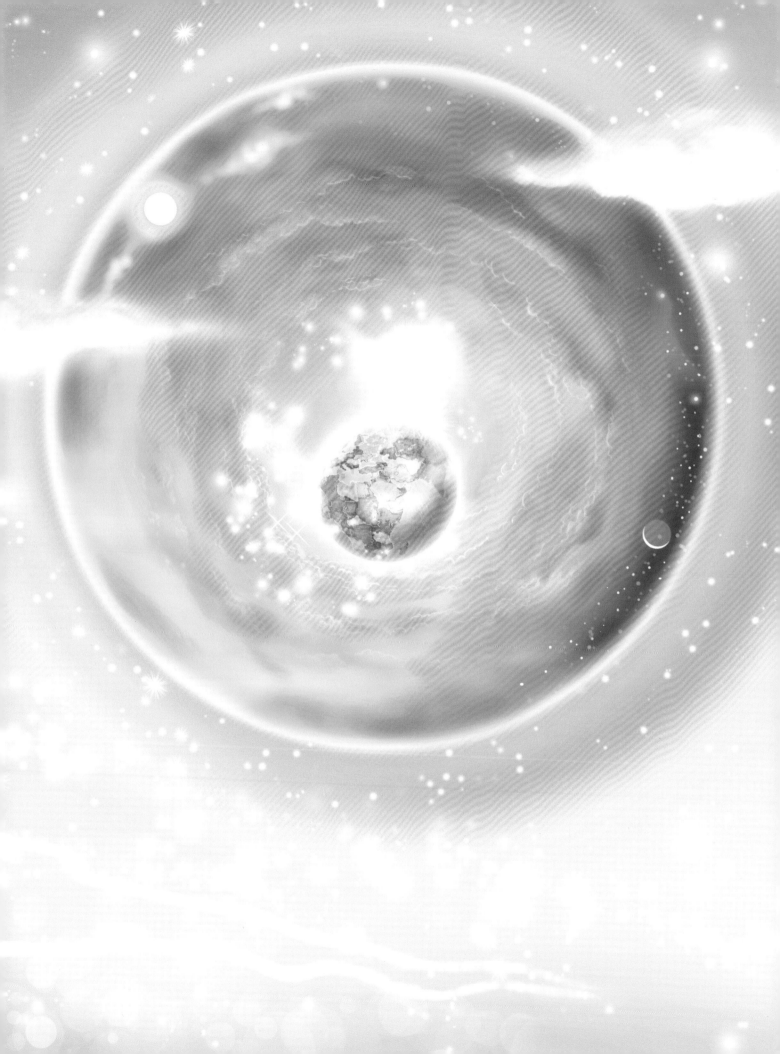

Everyone eagerly awaited the birth of the new child.

There was much happiness in the home and many beautiful gifts
had arrived from family and friends.

ut the Lord also wanted to
give gifts to celebrate the soul's birth.

The Lord knew that many people in the world
had forgotten Him, and He wanted this little soul
to remind the people of the oneness
of the Lord with all things.

So just before it was born, the Lord sent for
the soul to give it the gifts it would one day
share with the people of the world.

At first, the soul saw the Lord as a shining stream of song, flowing as far as the eye could see! Then out of the stream, the Lord formed himself into a majestic Being of Light! He scooped the Little Soul up into his arms and said, "Come with me, Little Soul, and learn how the One becomes the many."

Then the Lord splashed into the shimmering stream, sending musical waves of light high into the air! He swung onto a great glowing note and off they sailed, thrilling the Little Soul through and through!

They sailed through the dreamy pastel colours of the heavens
and swept through the scattering stars of the inner skies. The stream's swift current
carried them farther and farther within, toward the centre of all that is and will ever be!
On and on they journeyed, through the deepest darkest unknown regions, gliding
right through the gossamer veils that keep each realm a secret from the last.

And when they had gone beyond beyond and sailed into the first shining
mists of pure spirit, they rounded the last bend....

There they beheld a great sparkling sea of light,
the clearest brightest light one could ever imagine!

Round and round they turned...
seeing nothing but the luminous light of the Lord's Being
that went on forever and ever –

And the Little Soul could feel that the sea of light
was made of endless love and peace and nothing more.

"I am One Light," said the Lord...

"...but on earth my One Light shines out through many lamps."

Then the Lord pointed off in the distance and there the soul could see the world, glowing in the starry deep dark of space!

"Look closer..." said the Lord.

So the Little Soul looked closer... and soon it could see that every tiny atom of the creation was a shining lamp of light! And then the Little Soul knew... that the stars, the skies, the earth and everything in it were all made of the One Light of the Lord.

This made the Little Soul feel happy and safe and right at home.

I must always remember, thought the Little Soul,
that it is the Lord's One Light shining out
through all the many different
lanterns of his creation.

"ONE LIGHT, MANY LAMPS"

...said the Little Soul,
so it could remember what it had learned
and one day share it with the people of the world.

"Listen, little one,
to the sound of my light,"
said the Lord.

The soul began to hear the sound of the light
as it flowed out into the rainbow colours of the
creation, giving everything life. The thrilling sound
made the Little Soul want to sing and
dance and jump for joy!

"I am One Sound," said the Lord, "but on
earth my One Sound becomes many songs."

The soul began to hear the song of the earth
spinning through space and the singing of the
stars in the heavens. It could hear the whistling
song of the winter wind and the gentle song
of spring rain falling upon new leaves.

The soul heard the songs of the splashing
streams and the roaring waves of the sea.

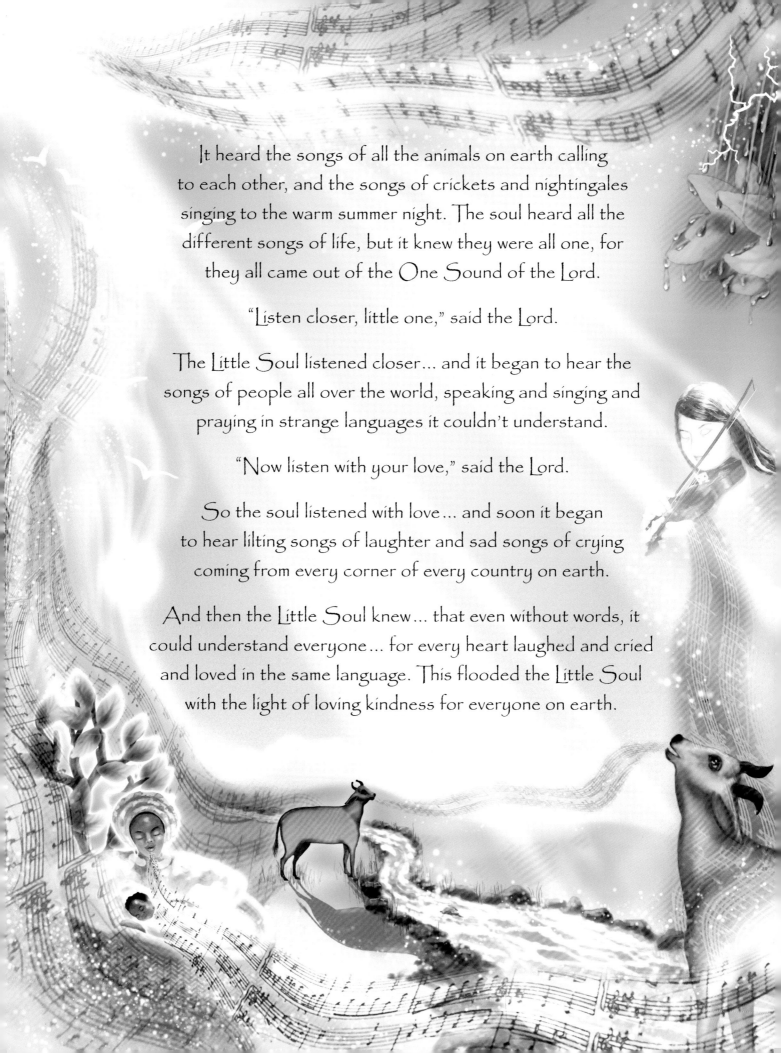

It heard the songs of all the animals on earth calling to each other, and the songs of crickets and nightingales singing to the warm summer night. The soul heard all the different songs of life, but it knew they were all one, for they all came out of the One Sound of the Lord.

"Listen closer, little one," said the Lord.

The Little Soul listened closer... and it began to hear the songs of people all over the world, speaking and singing and praying in strange languages it couldn't understand.

"Now listen with your love," said the Lord.

So the soul listened with love... and soon it began to hear lilting songs of laughter and sad songs of crying coming from every corner of every country on earth.

And then the Little Soul knew... that even without words, it could understand everyone... for every heart laughed and cried and loved in the same language. This flooded the Little Soul with the light of loving kindness for everyone on earth.

I must always remember, thought the Little Soul,
to listen with my love to every song I hear, for
every atom of creation is singing the
same One Sound of the Lord.

"ONE LIGHT, MANY LAMPS

ONE SOUND, MANY SONGS"

...said the Little Soul,
so it could remember what it had learned
and one day share it with the people of the world.

"**C**ome on! Let's go!" said the Lord.

In the blink of an eye, they streaked through the stars and swept into a splendid secret hiding place. With a wave of his hand, the Lord opened a window in the glistening veil of golden mist to reveal the earth on the other side! There, wondrous wild animals roamed the grasslands.

"Understand, little one," the Lord whispered, so as not to frighten the animals,
"I am the One Creator, but on earth I become many creatures."

The Little Soul was overjoyed to see that all the creatures were made out of the
great sound and light of the Lord's Being, and that the Creator
himself was playing the part of every creature on earth!

I must always remember, thought the Little Soul,
to be gentle and kind to every creature
in the creation, for the Lord himself
lives inside each and every one.

"ONE LIGHT, MANY LAMPS

ONE SOUND, MANY SONGS

ONE CREATOR, MANY CREATURES"

...said the Little Soul,
so it could remember what it had learned
and one day share it with the people of the world.

"**H**ang on tightly, little one!" said the Lord as they soared up to a great towering cliff.

From here, the soul could see the light and sound surging out from the great Source of all being in a gigantic thundering waterfall of ringing radiance!

"I am One Power!" said the Lord above the roaring wonder, "but on earth, my One Power becomes many people."

The Little Soul looked down and saw the One Power of the Lord cascading down into the world, giving life to all the people and shining brightly in their eyes and hearts!

Even though the people all looked like separate beings of many colours, shapes and sizes, the little soul was delighted to discover that they were really only one being!

And then the Little Soul knew... that the Lord himself had secretly come to earth, to play the part of every person of every nation!

I must always remember, thought the Little Soul,
to love the One Lord, who shines
inside every person in every
country on earth.

"ONE LIGHT, MANY LAMPS

ONE SOUND, MANY SONGS

ONE CREATOR, MANY CREATURES

ONE POWER, MANY PEOPLE"

...said the Little Soul,
so it could remember what it had learned
and one day share it with the people of the world.

"Come on! Let's go!" said the Lord, taking the Little Soul on a wild ride down the resplendent waterfall of light and sound.

When they reached the sky above the earth, they stopped and hovered there amongst the peaceful pink clouds.

"I am One Love, my child," said the Lord, "but on earth my love becomes many lanes."

The Little Soul looked down and saw people from all over the world walking upon many different lanes upon the earth. And every lane led to the same one temple of light!

The Lord and the Soul silently drifted down closer and closer... and then slipped right inside the temple itself!

Once inside…
the Little Soul saw that
the temple of light was love for the
Lord, shining in the heart of everyone.

The soul saw that those who entered here from
all the different lanes ascended a single staircase of
light… together. And then the Little Soul knew that it was
here that all lanes to the Lord become one – the lane of love….

I must always remember, thought the Little Soul,
that it makes no difference which lane one
walks to worship the Lord, for all lanes
are good that lead to love for Him.

"ONE LIGHT, MANY LAMPS

ONE SOUND, MANY SONGS

ONE CREATOR, MANY CREATURES

ONE POWER, MANY PEOPLE

ONE LOVE, MANY LANES"

...said the Little Soul,
so it could remember what it had learned
and one day share it with the people of the world.

At that very moment, the light, sound, power and love of the Creator slowly began to whirl round and round until they were all one... then became still... a blinding brilliance, radiating endless rays of bliss and peace.

"Behold the One!" said the Lord.

The Little Soul was awestruck and astonished and instantly filled with boundless joy. But it soon began to worry... How would it ever find words big or bright or beautiful enough to describe such wonder?

The Lord, who hears all things, heard the silent cry hidden in the heart of the Little Soul.

"Do not worry what words you
will use, little one," he said softly.
"I live in the world in the form of love.

I have filled you with my love and
my love will speak for you. I will share
my gifts of oneness through your
loving thoughts and words and
all that you do.

And the people of the world will be
happy that you have reminded them
of what they had forgotten."

The Lord looked down at the Little Soul for a long moment and finally spoke again.

"Now that you have learned how the One becomes the many, the time has come for you to go, little one, and take your place in the world. They are eagerly awaiting your arrival."

The Little Soul bowed deeply, then whispered, "Thank you for giving me your gifts of oneness. I am ready now to go, but I am very sad to leave."

The Lord beamed down on the Little Soul like warm golden sunshine. "Remember," he said softly, "I am always with you. And one day, I will show you the way to return back home from the many to the One."

Happy now and at peace, the soul smiled. The Lord gently passed his great radiant hand across the face of the Little Soul, blessing it, until it shone as brightly as the noonday sun.

**V**ery soon, a splendid celebration began on earth!

A child had been born, a peaceful child whose face seemed to glow with radiance, bliss and hidden wonder.

The new baby lay sound asleep, but deep inside…

...the soul of the baby was wide awake,
remembering the Lord and giving
thanks for his great gifts
one by one...

"One Light, many lamps
One Sound, many songs
One Creator, many creatures
One Power, many people
One Love, many lanes"

...said the Little Soul,
so it could remember
what it had learned and one day
share it with the people of the world.

Many Lamps